CGP

Maths

Key Stage 2
For ages 9-10

Practise & Learn

Published by CGP

Editors:
Joe Brazier
David Broadbent
Josephine Gibbons

Updated by Rob Harrison, Simon Little and Ben Train

With thanks to David Ryan for the proofreading.

ISBN: 978 1 84762 740 7

Printed by Elanders Ltd, Newcastle upon Tyne
Clipart from Corel®

Contents

Place Value & Ordering 4

Written Addition 6

Written Subtraction 7

Written Multiplication 8

Written Division 10

Multiply/Divide by 10s 12

Factors 13

Multiples 14

Prime Numbers 15

Fractions 16

More Fractions 18

Fractions, Decimals and Percentages 20

Problem Solving 22

Rounding and Estimating 24

Units and Measures 25

Perimeter, Area and Volume 26

Angles 28

Tables and Charts 30

Reflections 32

Place Value & Ordering

Numbers can be written using words or Roman numerals.

1 106 253 is the same as:

one million, one hundred and six thousand, **two hundred** and **fifty-three**

M = 1000   D = 500   C = 100   L = 50   X = 10   V = 5   I = 1

Digits that are the same are added. ➪ **XX = 10 + 10 = 20**

Small digits after big ones are added. ➪ **CVI = 100 + 5 + 1 = 106**

Small digits before big ones are subtracted. ➪ **XLI = 50 – 10 + 1 = 41**

Write the value of the **bold** number in words.

2 **8**31 192

| eight hundred thousand |

6 1**7**0 451

| |

4 199 805

| |

3 25**1** 580

| |

Write these words as numbers.

Six million, two hundred and sixty-two thousand, four hundred and ninety.

| 6 262 490 |

Three million, five hundred thousand, six hundred and fifty-two.

| |

Write these roman numerals as numbers.

MM | 2000 | DXI | | CCLX | |

XIV | 14 | CDI | | XXVI | |

CMLII | 952 | MMXV | | MCDIV | |

Ascending means the numbers are ordered from lowest to highest.

lowest ➞ highest			
0.99	5.9	7	9.5

Descending means ordering the numbers highest to lowest.

highest ➞ lowest			
9.5	7	5.9	0.99

Put each group of numbers below into ascending order.

5.09   5.1   ~~0.85~~
~~1.05~~   2.89

0.85	1.05			

1 295 615   78 075
3 152 986   812 266

0.543   0.653
0.54   0.054

Put each group of numbers below into descending order.

~~9.11~~   ~~9.18~~   8.81
7.9   8.05

9.18	9.11			

32   4.313   3.3
4.4   304

2 550 980   55 995
925 500   2 553 411

Use each rule to continue each descending or ascending sequence.

Rule:	Subtract 0.1	0.62	0.52				
Rule:	Add 1.02	1.98	3				
Rule:	Add 0.3	− 0.8	− 0.5				

5

Written Addition

You can make adding up big numbers simpler by carrying over digits between the place value columns. Here's an example:

Put the numbers in a column. Make sure the place value columns line up.

```
  3 2 7 1 9
+   4 1 5 9
───────────
  3 6 8 7 8
          1
```

Add up the numbers in each column from right to left.

Carry the left-hand digit to the next column if the answer is more than 9. E.g. **9 + 9 = 18**

Use the carrying over method to answer these sums.

```
  9 8 2 1
+   1 4 9
─────────
  9 9 7 0
        1
```

```
  2 9 9 0
+ 1 3 0 1
─────────
```

```
  6 1 7 4 3
+   1 4 1 2
───────────
```

```
  7 2 0 9 8
+ 1 4 2 1 5
───────────
```

```
  8 6 5 5
+   2 3 5
─────────
```

```
  5 1 6 2
+ 2 3 9 9
─────────
```

```
  3 6 2 5 8
+   5 0 6 1
───────────
```

```
  4 8 5 1 5
+ 1 5 2 0 7
───────────
```

Answer these questions using the carrying over method.

34.5 + 9.12

```
    3 4 . 5
+    9 . 1 2
───────────
    4 3 . 6 2
            1
```

81.53 + 13.29

33.9 + 21.11

6.25 + 1.85

Written Subtraction

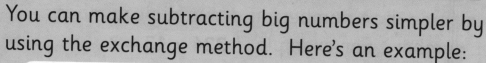

You can make subtracting big numbers simpler by using the exchange method. Here's an example:

Put the numbers in a column, lining up the place value columns.

$$
\begin{array}{r}
{}^{3}\ \ \ \ {}^{8} \\
4\,{}^{1}6\,8\,9\,{}^{1}3 \\
-\ 7\,2\,5\,6 \\
\hline
3\,9\,6\,3\,7
\end{array}
$$

If you have to subtract a bigger number from a smaller number, make an exchange from the next place value column.

Subtract the numbers in each column from right to left.

Use the exchange method to answer these subtractions.

$$
\begin{array}{r}
{}^{5} \\
5\,\cancel{6}\,{}^{1}1 \\
-\ 3\,3\,7 \\
\hline
2\,2\,4
\end{array}
$$

$$
\begin{array}{r}
7\,1\,7\,1 \\
-\ \ 1\,5\,2 \\
\hline

\end{array}
$$

$$
\begin{array}{r}
7\,4\,7\,3 \\
-\ 5\,3\,6\,8 \\
\hline

\end{array}
$$

$$
\begin{array}{r}
8\,8\,4\,6\,2 \\
-\ 6\,9\,3\,4\,5 \\
\hline

\end{array}
$$

Answer these questions using the exchange method.

526 – 217

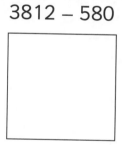

$$
\begin{array}{r}
{}^{1} \\
5\,\cancel{2}\,{}^{1}6 \\
-\ 2\,1\,7 \\
\hline
3\,0\,9
\end{array}
$$

3812 – 580

61577 – 3484

24295 – 2316

Use the exchange method to answer to these questions.

A log is 94.25 cm long. A beaver eats 23.45 cm of it. How much is left?

Ann's walk to school is 876.25 m. This morning she has walked 395.5 m. How far does she have left to walk?

Written Multiplication

When you multiply a three digit number by a two digit number, partition the smaller number. For example: **324 × 13 = ?**

Step 1: Find 324 × 3.

```
    3 2 4
  ×   1 3
    9 7 2
      1
```

Multiply 4, 20 and 300 by 3.

Carry the 1 from the 12 onto the next column.

Step 2: Find 324 × 10.

```
    3 2 4
  ×   1 3
    9 7 2
      1
  3 2 4 0
```

Multiply 4, 20 and 300 by 10.

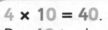 **4 × 10 = 40.** Put **40** in the correct columns.

Step 3: Add the two numbers together to get the final answer.

```
    9 7 2
  + 3 2 4 0
    4 2 1 2
      1 1
```

Complete these multiplications using the spaces below.

```
      9 1
  ×   4 2
  ─────────
      1 8 2
  + 3 6 4 0
  ─────────
    3 8 2 2
        1
```

```
      4 3
  ×   3 5
  ─────────



  ─────────

```

```
      2 9
  ×   2 4
  ─────────



  ─────────

```

```
      5 1
  ×   4 7
  ─────────



  ─────────

```

```
    1 6 2
  ×    3 9
  ─────────



  ─────────

```

```
    2 1 5
  ×    4 4
  ─────────



  ─────────

```

```
  2 4 1 3
  ×     2 3
  ─────────



  ─────────

```

```
  4 0 1 5
  ×     3 6
  ─────────



  ─────────

```

Solve these multiplication problems. Show your working.

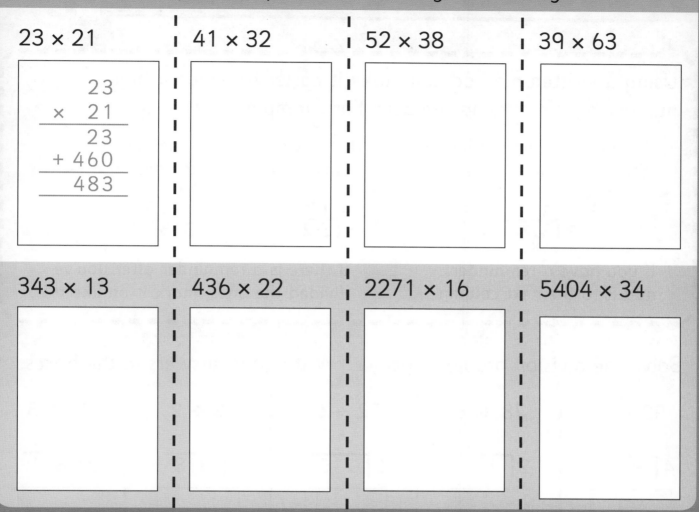

| 23 × 21 | 41 × 32 | 52 × 38 | 39 × 63 |

```
      23
  ×   21
  ───────
      23
  +  460
  ───────
     483
```

| 343 × 13 | 436 × 22 | 2271 × 16 | 5404 × 34 |

Solve these multiplication problems using written multiplication.

1 spoon holds
25 ml of water.
How much water
will 85 spoons hold?

Bob has 430 blocks
that each weigh 35 g.
How much do they
weigh in total?

1 guitar costs
£675. How
much will 23
guitars cost?

Written Division

Using a written method can make it easier to divide a bigger number by a one digit number. For example: **521 ÷ 3 = ?**

Divide each number by **3**. Start with the hundreds...

... then divide the tens by **3**...

... then divide the ones by **3**.

$$\begin{array}{r} 1 \\ 3\overline{)5^2 2\ 1} \end{array}$$

$$\begin{array}{r} 17 \\ 3\overline{)5^2 2^1 1} \end{array}$$

$$\begin{array}{r} 17\ 3\ \text{r}\ 2 \\ 3\overline{)5^2 2^1 1} \end{array}$$

If you have a remainder, add it to the next column.

If there is a remainder after you've divided the ones, mark it on like this.

Solve the division problems below. Write your answers in the boxes.

92 ÷ 4	78 ÷ 2	72 ÷ 6	38 ÷ 2	81 ÷ 3
$\begin{array}{r} 2\ 3 \\ 4\overline{)9\ ^1 2} \end{array}$	$2\overline{)7\ 8}$	$6\overline{)7\ 2}$	$2\overline{)3\ 8}$	$3\overline{)8\ 1}$
23				

64 ÷ 4	75 ÷ 5	59 ÷ 3	98 ÷ 8	79 ÷ 4
$4\overline{)6\ 4}$	$5\overline{)7\ 5}$	$3\overline{)5\ 9}$	$8\overline{)9\ 8}$	$4\overline{)7\ 9}$

---

90 bones are shared between some dogs.
Work out the number of bones each dog will get.

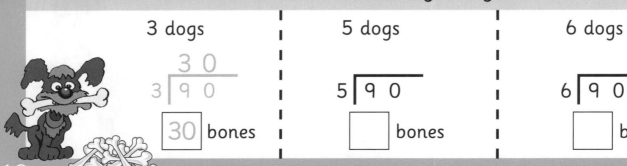

3 dogs	5 dogs	6 dogs
$\begin{array}{r} 3\ 0 \\ 3\overline{)9\ 0} \end{array}$	$5\overline{)9\ 0}$	$6\overline{)9\ 0}$
30 bones	___ bones	___ bones

10

Solve the division problems below. Write your answers in the boxes.

104 ÷ 4

$$\begin{array}{r} 0\ 2\ 6 \\ 4\overline{\smash{)}1\ ^1 0\ ^2 4} \end{array}$$

26

134 ÷ 2

240 ÷ 4

165 ÷ 5

336 ÷ 6

472 ÷ 8

942 ÷ 6

747 ÷ 3

4544 ÷ 4

6863 ÷ 2

2445 ÷ 8

5510 ÷ 9

Solve these real life division problems. You'll need to decide whether to round your answer up or down.

Danik needs 615 books.
Books are packed in boxes of 4.
How many boxes should he get?

$$\begin{array}{r} 1\ 5\ 3\ r\ 3 \\ 4\overline{\smash{)}6\ ^2 1\ ^1 5} \end{array}$$ Round up:

154 boxes

221 people want to go sailing.
Each boat can fit 8 people.
How many boats are needed?

Umbrellas cost £6.
Rob has £308. How many umbrellas can he buy?

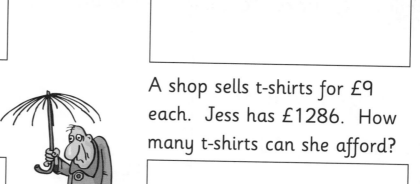

A shop sells t-shirts for £9 each. Jess has £1286. How many t-shirts can she afford?

11

Multiply/Divide by 10s

To multiply by 10, 100 or 1000 move the digits to the left along the place value columns. To divide, move the digits to the right.

Move **one** space **left** to multiply by **10**.

T	O
	2
× 10	
= 2	0

Move **two** spaces **left** to multiply by **100**.

H	T	O	t
		1	6
× 100			
= 1	6	0	

Move **three** spaces **right** to divide by **1000**.

H	T	O	t	h
1	3	0		
÷ 1000				
=		0	1	3

Fill in the boxes to complete the multiplications.

51	×	100	=	5100		35	×	1000	=
7	×	1000	=			0.5	×	100	=
82	×	10	=			1.67	×	10	=
40	×	100	=			0.8	×	1000	=

Fill in the boxes to complete the divisions.

8.7	÷	10	=	0.87		509	÷	100	=
6500	÷	1000	=			12.7	÷	10	=
482	÷	10	=			0.8	÷	10	=
9	÷	100	=			70	÷	1000	=
270	÷	1000	=			631	÷	100	=

Factors

Factor pairs are two factors of a number that multiply together to make that number. For example:

> The factors pairs of 10 are:
> **1 × 10** and **2 × 5**

> The factors of 10 are:
> 1, **2**, 5 and **10**

A common factor of two numbers is a factor of both numbers:

> The factors of 15 are:
> 1, **3**, 5 and **15**

> The common factors
> of 10 and 15 are:
> 1 and **5**

List all the factor pairs for each number given below.
Use the factor pairs to list all the factors of each number.

20
1 × 20
2 × 10
4 × 5
1, 2, 4, 5, 10 and 20

15

28

List the factors of each number.
Then write their common factors in the box underneath.

40 and 24

Factors of 40:
1 2 4 5 8 10 20 40
Factors of 24:

Common factors: [ ]

30 and 18

Common factors: [ ]

Multiples

A common multiple of two numbers is a number that's a multiple of both numbers. Here's an example:

20 is a common multiple of **5** and **10** because **5** × 4 = **20** and **10** × 2 = **20**

Answer the questions below.

The first ten multiples of 4 are:

The first ten multiples of 6 are:

Three common multiples
of 4 and 6 are:

Find two common multiples for each pair of numbers given below.

2 and 4
4   8
Two times table:
2 ④ 6 ⑧
Four times table:
④   ⑧

3 and 5

6 and 10

6 and 8

4 and 7

14

Prime Numbers

A prime number will only divide by **1** and **itself**. Here are the prime numbers up to 20:

2, 3, 5, 7, 11, 13, 17, 19
If it divides by anything that isn't 1 or itself, it isn't prime.

You can split whole numbers into **prime factors**. These are just factors that are prime numbers.

Write 6 as a product of prime factors. $6 = 2 \times 3$

Write 18 as a product of prime factors. $18 = 2 \times 3 \times 3$

Circle the prime number in each box below

15	33	38	
24	50	19	

27		16	
	31		9
42		18	

4	18		43
82	30		56

Draw a line from the start of the maze to the finish.
You can only pass through prime numbers.

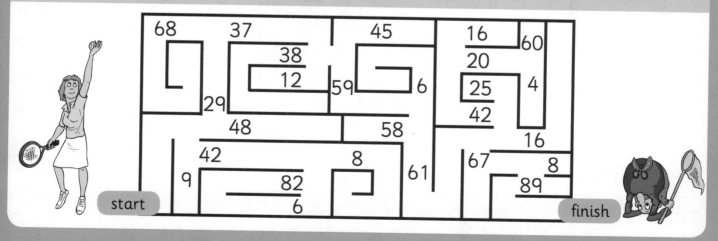

Write each number below as a product of prime factors.

15 = ☐ × ☐   28 = ☐ × ☐ × ☐

15

Fractions

Multiply or divide the **numerator** and **denominator** by the same number to get an equivalent fraction. For example:

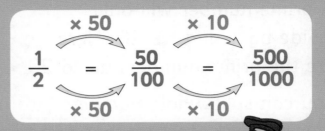

$$\frac{1}{2} \;=\; \frac{50}{100} \;=\; \frac{500}{1000}$$

Fill in the boxes to complete the equivalent fractions and show how you calculated them.

$$\frac{2}{4} = \frac{1}{\boxed{2}} \qquad \frac{5}{15} = \frac{\square}{3} \qquad \frac{2}{3} = \frac{6}{\square} \qquad \frac{1}{5} = \frac{\square}{1000}$$

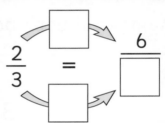

Circle the fractions that are equivalent to the **bold** fraction.

$\frac{1}{3}$

$\frac{3}{9}$ (circled)　$\frac{4}{12}$　$\frac{3}{8}$

$\frac{7}{23}$　$\frac{4}{16}$　$\frac{6}{15}$

$\frac{5}{15}$　$\frac{6}{18}$

$\frac{800}{1000}$

$\frac{8}{100}$　$\frac{80}{100}$　$\frac{8000}{100}$

$\frac{4}{5}$　$\frac{4}{13}$　$\frac{8}{10}$

$\frac{10}{20}$　$\frac{9}{20}$　$\frac{19}{18}$

Fill in the blanks below to make some equivalent fractions.

$$\frac{3}{4} = \frac{\boxed{9}}{12} \qquad \frac{17}{100} = \frac{170}{\square} \qquad \frac{24}{36} = \frac{\square}{6} \qquad \frac{940}{1000} = \frac{\square}{100}$$

Practise and Learn

Maths

Ages 9-10

Answers

This section shows each of the pages from the book with the answers filled in.

The pages are laid out in the same way as the book itself, so the questions can be easily marked by you, or by your child.

There are also helpful learning tips with some of the pages.

4

Place Value & Ordering

Numbers can be written using words or Roman numerals.

1 106 253 is the same as: **one million**, one hundred and six thousand, two hundred and fifty-three

M = 1000   D = 500   C = 100   L = 50   X = 10   V = 5   I = 1

Digits that are the same are added. ➡ XX = 10 + 10 = **20**
Small digits after big ones are added. ➡ CVI = 100 + 5 + 1 = **106**
Small digits before big ones are subtracted. ➡ XLI = 50 – 10 + 1 = **41**

Write the value of the bold number in words.

2 **8**31 192	6 1**7**0 451
eight hundred thousand	**seventy thousand**
4 199 805	3 251 5**8**0
four million	**one thousand**

Write these words as numbers.

Six million, two hundred and sixty-two thousand, four hundred and ninety.	6 262 490
Three million, five hundred thousand, six hundred and fifty-two.	**3 500 652**

Write these roman numerals as numbers.

MM	2000	DXI	**511**	CCLX	**260**
XIV	14	CDI	**401**	XXVI	**26**
CMLII	952	MMXV	**2015**	MCDIV	**1404**

4

If your child struggles with Roman numerals, try asking them to tell the time on a clock using Roman numerals.

5

Ascending means the numbers are ordered from lowest to highest. ➡ lowest ➡ highest 0.99 5.9 7 9.5
Descending means ordering the numbers highest to lowest. ➡ highest ➡ lowest 9.5 7 5.9 0.99

Put each group of numbers below into ascending order.

5.09 5.1 ~~0.85~~ 1.05 2.89	0.85	1.05	**2.89**	**5.09**	**5.1**
1 295 615 78 075 3 152 986 812 266	**78 075**	**812 266**	**1 295 615**	**3 152 986**	
0.543 0.653 0.54 0.054	**0.054**	**0.54**	**0.543**	**0.653**	

Put each group of numbers below into descending order.

~~9.11~~ ~~9.18~~ 8.81 7.9 8.05	9.18	9.11	**8.81**	**8.05**	**7.9**
32 4.313 3.3 4.4 304	**304**	**32**	**4.4**	**4.313**	**3.3**
2 550 980 55 995 925 500 2 553 411	**2 553 411**	**2 550 980**	**925 500**	**55 995**	

Use each rule to continue each descending or ascending sequence.

Rule:	Subtract 0.1	0.62	0.52	**0.42**	**0.32**	**0.22**	**0.12**
Rule:	Add 1.02	1.98	3	**4.02**	**5.04**	**6.06**	**7.08**
Rule:	Add 0.3	– 0.8	– 0.5	**– 0.2**	**0.1**	**0.4**	**0.7**

5

If your child has difficulty with number sequences and negative numbers, try getting them to write out a number line which they can use to count on or back.

Written Addition

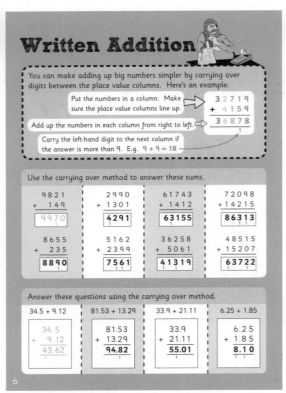

You can make adding up big numbers simpler by carrying over digits between the place value columns. Here's an example:

Put the numbers in a column. Make sure the place value columns line up.

$$\begin{array}{r} 3\,2\,7\,1\,9 \\ +\ \ 4\,1\,5\,9 \\ \hline 3\,6\,8\,7\,8 \\ {\scriptstyle 1} \end{array}$$

Add up the numbers in each column from right to left.

Carry the left-hand digit to the next column if the answer is more than 9. E.g. 9 + 9 = 18

Use the carrying over method to answer these sums.

9821 + 149 = **9970**	2990 + 1301 = **4291**	61743 + 1412 = **63155**	72098 + 14215 = **86313**
8655 + 235 = **8890**	5162 + 2399 = **7561**	36258 + 5061 = **41319**	48515 + 15207 = **63722**

Answer these questions using the carrying over method.

34.5 + 9.12	81.53 + 13.29	33.9 + 21.11	6.25 + 1.85
34.5 + 9.12 = **43.62**	81.53 + 13.29 = **94.82**	33.9 + 21.11 = **55.01**	6.25 + 1.85 = **8.10**

For more practice, ask your child to add up the cost of items on your shopping receipts.

Written Subtraction

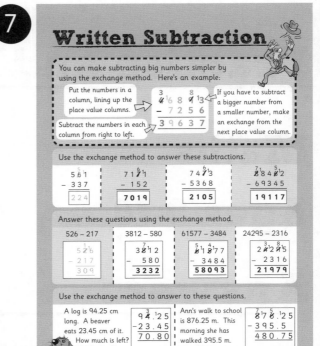

You can make subtracting big numbers simpler by using the exchange method. Here's an example:

Put the numbers in a column, lining up the place value columns.

$$\begin{array}{r} 4\,6\,8\,9\,{}^{1}3 \\ -\ \ 7\,2\,5\,6 \\ \hline 3\,9\,6\,3\,7 \end{array}$$

Subtract the numbers in each column from right to left.

If you have to subtract a bigger number from a smaller number, make an exchange from the next place value column.

Use the exchange method to answer these subtractions.

561 − 337 = **224**	7171 − 152 = **7019**	7473 − 5368 = **2105**	88462 − 69345 = **19117**

Answer these questions using the exchange method.

526 − 217	3812 − 580	61577 − 3484	24295 − 2316
526 − 217 = **309**	3812 − 580 = **3232**	61577 − 3484 = **58093**	24295 − 2316 = **21979**

Use the exchange method to answer to these questions.

A log is 94.25 cm long. A beaver eats 23.45 cm of it. How much is left?

$$\begin{array}{r} 9\,4.2\,5 \\ -\ 2\,3.4\,5 \\ \hline 7\,0.8\,0 \end{array}$$

70.8 cm

Ann's walk to school is 876.25 m. This morning she has walked 395.5 m. How far does she have left to walk?

$$\begin{array}{r} 8\,7\,6.2\,5 \\ -\ 3\,9\,5.5 \\ \hline 4\,8\,0.7\,5 \end{array}$$

480.75 m

Written Multiplication

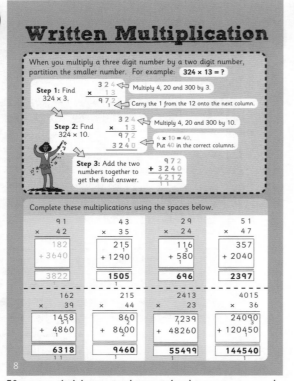

When you multiply a three digit number by a two digit number, partition the smaller number. For example: **324 × 13 = ?**

Step 1: Find 324 × 3.

$$\begin{array}{r} 3\,2\,4 \\ \times\ \ 1\,3 \\ \hline 9\,7\,2 \end{array}$$

Multiply 4, 20 and 300 by 3.

Carry the 1 from the 12 onto the next column.

Step 2: Find 324 × 10.

$$\begin{array}{r} 3\,2\,4 \\ \times\ \ 1\,3 \\ \hline 9\,7\,2 \\ 3\,2\,4\,0 \end{array}$$

Multiply 4, 20 and 300 by 10.

4 × 10 = 40. Put 40 in the correct columns.

Step 3: Add the two numbers together to get the final answer.

$$\begin{array}{r} 9\,7\,2 \\ +\ 3\,2\,4\,0 \\ \hline 4\,2\,1\,2 \end{array}$$

Complete these multiplications using the spaces below.

91 × 42	43 × 35	29 × 24	51 × 47
182 + 3640 = **3822**	215 + 1290 = **1505**	116 + 580 = **696**	357 + 2040 = **2397**

162 × 39	215 × 44	2413 × 23	4015 × 36
1458 + 4860 = **6318**	860 + 8600 = **9460**	7239 + 48260 = **55499**	24090 + 120450 = **144540**

If your child struggles with these pages, check that they fully understand the carrying over method of addition used on page 6.

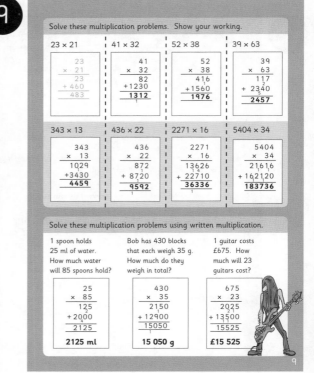

Solve these multiplication problems. Show your working.

23 × 21	41 × 32	52 × 38	39 × 63
23 + 460 = **483**	82 + 1230 = **1312**	416 + 1560 = **1976**	117 + 2340 = **2457**

343 × 13	436 × 22	2271 × 16	5404 × 34
1029 + 3430 = **4459**	872 + 8720 = **9592**	13626 + 22710 = **36336**	21616 + 162120 = **183736**

Solve these multiplication problems using written multiplication.

1 spoon holds 25 ml of water. How much water will 85 spoons hold?

$$\begin{array}{r} 2\,5 \\ \times\ \ 8\,5 \\ \hline 1\,2\,5 \\ +\ 2\,0\,0\,0 \\ \hline 2\,1\,2\,5 \end{array}$$

2125 ml

Bob has 430 blocks that each weigh 35 g. How much do they weigh in total?

$$\begin{array}{r} 4\,3\,0 \\ \times\ \ 3\,5 \\ \hline 2\,1\,5\,0 \\ +\ 1\,2\,9\,0\,0 \\ \hline 1\,5\,0\,5\,0 \end{array}$$

15 050 g

1 guitar costs £675. How much will 23 guitars cost?

$$\begin{array}{r} 6\,7\,5 \\ \times\ \ 2\,3 \\ \hline 2\,0\,2\,5 \\ +\ 1\,3\,5\,0\,0 \\ \hline 1\,5\,5\,2\,5 \end{array}$$

£15 525

Written Division

Using a written method can make it easier to divide a bigger number by a one digit number. For example: **521 ÷ 3 = ?**

Divide each number by 3. Start with the hundreds...

$\frac{1}{3\,|\,5^2 2\,1}$

... then divide the tens by 3...

$\frac{1\,7}{3\,|\,5^2 2^1 1}$

... then divide the ones by 3.

$\frac{1\,7\,3\,r\,2}{3\,|\,5^2 2^1 1}$

If you have a remainder, add it to the next column.

If there is a remainder after you've divided the ones, mark it on like this.

Solve the division problems below. Write your answers in the boxes.

92 ÷ 4	78 ÷ 2	72 ÷ 6	38 ÷ 2	81 ÷ 3
$\frac{2\,3}{4\,|\,9\,2}$	$\frac{3\,9}{2\,|\,7\,^18}$	$\frac{1\,2}{6\,|\,7\,^12}$	$\frac{1\,9}{2\,|\,3\,^18}$	$\frac{2\,7}{3\,|\,8\,^21}$
23	**39**	**12**	**19**	**27**

64 ÷ 4	75 ÷ 5	59 ÷ 3	98 ÷ 8	79 ÷ 4
$\frac{1\,6}{4\,|\,6\,^24}$	$\frac{1\,5}{5\,|\,7\,^25}$	$\frac{1\,9\,r\,2}{3\,|\,5\,^29}$	$\frac{1\,2\,r\,2}{8\,|\,9\,^18}$	$\frac{1\,9\,r\,3}{4\,|\,7\,^39}$
16	**15**	**19 r 2**	**12 r 2**	**19 r 3**

90 bones are shared between some dogs.
Work out the number of bones each dog will get.

3 dogs	5 dogs	6 dogs
$\frac{3\,0}{3\,|\,9\,0}$	$\frac{1\,8}{5\,|\,9\,^40}$	$\frac{1\,5}{6\,|\,9\,^30}$
30 bones	**18** bones	**15** bones

Solve the division problems below. Write your answers in the boxes.

104 ÷ 4	134 ÷ 2	240 ÷ 4	165 ÷ 5
$\frac{0\,2\,6}{4\,|\,1\,^10\,^24}$	$\frac{0\,6\,7}{2\,|\,1\,^13\,^14}$	$\frac{0\,6\,0}{4\,|\,2\,^24\,0}$	$\frac{0\,3\,3}{5\,|\,1\,^16\,^15}$
26	**67**	**60**	**33**

336 ÷ 6	472 ÷ 8	942 ÷ 6	747 ÷ 3
$\frac{0\,5\,6}{6\,|\,3\,^33\,^36}$	$\frac{0\,5\,9}{8\,|\,4\,^47\,^72}$	$\frac{1\,5\,7}{6\,|\,9\,^34\,^42}$	$\frac{2\,4\,9}{3\,|\,7\,^14\,^27}$
56	**59**	**157**	**249**

4544 ÷ 4	6863 ÷ 2	2445 ÷ 8	5510 ÷ 9
$\frac{1\,1\,3\,6}{4\,|\,4\,5\,^14\,^24}$	$\frac{3\,4\,3\,1\,r\,1}{2\,|\,6\,8\,6\,3}$	$\frac{0\,3\,0\,5\,r\,5}{8\,|\,2\,^24\,4\,^45}$	$\frac{0\,6\,1\,2\,r\,2}{9\,|\,5\,5\,^511\,^220}$
1136	**3431 r 1**	**305 r 5**	**612 r 2**

Solve these real life division problems. You'll need to decide whether to round your answer up or down.

Danik needs 615 books. Books are packed in boxes of 4. How many boxes should he get?

$\frac{1\,5\,3\,r\,3}{4\,|\,6\,^21\,^15}$ Round up: 154 boxes

221 people want to go sailing. Each boat can fit 8 people. How many boats are needed?

$\frac{0\,2\,7\,r\,5}{8\,|\,2\,^22\,^61}$ Round up: **28 boats**

Umbrellas cost £6. Rob has £308. How many umbrellas can he buy?

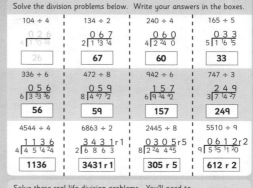

$\frac{0\,5\,1\,r\,2}{6\,|\,3\,^30\,8}$ Round down: **51 umbrellas**

A shop sells t-shirts for £9 each. Jess has £1286. How many t-shirts can she afford?

$\frac{0\,1\,4\,2\,r\,8}{9\,|\,1\,^12\,^38\,^26}$ Round down: **142 t-shirts**

Multiply/Divide by 10s

To multiply by 10, 100 or 1000 move the digits to the left along the place value columns. To divide, move the digits to the right.

Move **one space** left to multiply by **10**.

T	O
	2
= 2	0

$\times\,10$

Move **two spaces** left to multiply by **100**.

H	T	O	t
		1	6
= 1	6	0	

$\times\,100$

Move **three spaces** right to divide by **1000**.

H	T	O	t	h
1	3	0		
		0	1	3

$\div\,1000$

Fill in the boxes to complete the multiplications.

51	×	100	=	5100		35	×	1000	=	**35000**
7	×	1000	=	**7000**		0.5	×	100	=	**50**
82	×	10	=	**820**		1.67	×	10	=	**16.7**
40	×	100	=	**4000**		0.8	×	1000	=	**800**

Fill in the boxes to complete the divisions.

8.7	÷	10	=	0.87		509	÷	100	=	**5.09**
6500	÷	1000	=	**6.5**		12.7	÷	10	=	**1.27**
482	÷	10	=	**48.2**		0.8	÷	10	=	**0.08**
9	÷	100	=	**0.09**		70	÷	1000	=	**0.07**
270	÷	1000	=	**0.27**		631	÷	100	=	**6.31**

Factors

Factor pairs are two factors of a number that multiply together to make that number. For example:

The factors pairs of 10 are:
1 × 10   and   2 × 5

The factors of 10 are:
1, 2, 5 and 10

A common factor of two numbers is a factor of both numbers:

The factors of 15 are:
1, 3, 5 and 15

The common factors of 10 and 15 are:
1 and 5

List all the factor pairs for each number given below. Use the factor pairs to list all the factors of each number.

20
1 × 20
2 × 10
4 × 5
1, 2, 4, 5, 10 and 20

15
1 × 15
3 × 5
1, 3, 5 and 15

28
1 × 28
2 × 14
4 × 7
1, 2, 4, 7, 14 and 28

List the factors of each number. Then write their common factors in the box underneath.

40 and 24

Factors of 40:
①②④ 5 ⑧ 10 20 40

Factors of 24:
①② 3 ④ 6 ⑧ 12 24

Common factors: **1, 2, 4, 8**

30 and 18

Factors of 30:
①②③ 5 ⑥ 10 15 30

Factors of 18:
①②③⑥ 9 18

Common factors: **1, 2, 3, 6**

14 — Multiples

A common multiple of two numbers is a number that's a multiple of both numbers. Here's an example:

20 is a common multiple of 5 and 10 because 5 × 4 = 20 and 10 × 2 = 20

Answer the questions below.

The first ten multiples of 4 are:	4, 8, 12, 16, 20, 24, 28, 32, 36, 40
The first ten multiples of 6 are:	6, 12, 18, 24, 30, 36, 42, 48, 54, 60
Three common multiples of 4 and 6 are:	12 24 36

Find two common multiples for each pair of numbers given below.

2 and 4   4   8
Two times table:
2 (4) 6 (8)
Four times table:
(4) (8)

3 and 5   15   30
Three times table:
3 6 9 12 (15) 18 21 24 27 (30)
Five times table:
5 10 (15) 20 25 (30)

6 and 10   30   60
Six times table:
6 12 18 24 (30) 36 42 48 54 (60)
Ten times table:
10 20 (30) 40 50 (60)

6 and 8   24   48
Six times table:
6 12 18 (24) 30 36 42 (48)
Eight times table:
8 16 (24) 32 40 (48)

4 and 7   28   56
Four times table:
4 8 12 16 20 24 (28) 32 36 40 44 48 52 (56)
Seven times table:
7 14 21 (28) 35 42 49 (56)

14

Finding common multiples of two numbers is a good way for your child to practise their times tables. Try asking them to pick other pairs of numbers and see how many common multiples they can find.

15 — Prime Numbers

A prime number will only divide by 1 and itself. Here are the prime numbers up to 20:

2, 3, 5, 7, 11, 13, 17, 19
If it divides by anything that isn't 1 or itself, it isn't prime.

You can split whole numbers into **prime factors**. These are just factors that are prime numbers.

Write 6 as a product of prime factors. 6 = 2 × 3
Write 18 as a product of prime factors. 18 = 2 × 3 × 3

Circle the prime number in each box below

15 33 38	27 16	4 18 (43)
24 50 (19)	(31) 9 42 18	82 30 56

Draw a line from the start of the maze to the finish. You can only pass through prime numbers.

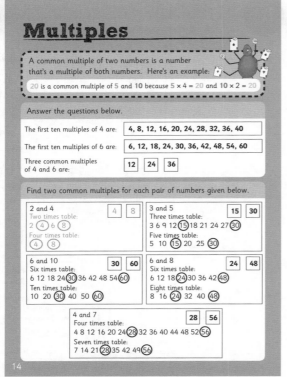

Write each number below as a product of prime factors.

15 = 3 × 5   28 = 2 × 2 × 7

15

16 — Fractions

Multiply or divide the **numerator** and **denominator** by the same number to get an equivalent fraction. For example:

$$\frac{1}{2} \xrightarrow{\times 50} \frac{50}{100} \xrightarrow{\times 10} \frac{500}{1000}$$

Fill in the boxes to complete the equivalent fractions and show how you calculated them.

$\frac{2}{4}$ (÷2) = $\frac{1}{2}$ (÷2)

$\frac{5}{15}$ (÷5) = $\frac{1}{3}$ (÷5)

$\frac{2}{3}$ (×3) = $\frac{6}{9}$ (×3)

$\frac{1}{5}$ (×200) = $\frac{200}{1000}$ (×200)

Circle the fractions that are equivalent to the **bold** fraction.

$\frac{1}{3}$ (3/9) (4/12) 3/8   7/23   4/16   6/15   (5/15) (6/18)

$\frac{800}{1000}$ 8/100 (80/100) 8000/100   4/5   4/13   (8/10)   10/20   9/20   19/18

Fill in the blanks below to make some equivalent fractions.

$\frac{3}{4} = \frac{9}{12}$ $\frac{17}{100} = \frac{170}{1000}$ $\frac{24}{36} = \frac{4}{6}$ $\frac{940}{1000} = \frac{94}{100}$

16

17

You can compare and order fractions by finding equivalent fractions. For example:

$\frac{4}{6}$ is bigger than $\frac{7}{12}$ because:
Fractions need the same denominator to be compared. $\frac{4}{6} = \frac{8}{12}$ is bigger than $\frac{7}{12}$.

Put these fractions in order from smallest to largest.

$\frac{1}{2}$ $\frac{1}{4}$ $\frac{3}{4}$ $\frac{3}{8}$
$\frac{1}{2} = \frac{4}{8}$ $\frac{1}{4} = \frac{2}{8}$ $\frac{3}{4} = \frac{6}{8}$ $\frac{3}{8}$

Smallest $\frac{1}{4}$ ⇨ $\frac{3}{8}$ ⇨ $\frac{1}{2}$ ⇨ $\frac{3}{4}$ Largest

$\frac{11}{20}$ $\frac{2}{5}$ $\frac{5}{10}$ $\frac{7}{10}$
$\frac{11}{20}$ $\frac{2}{5} = \frac{8}{20}$ $\frac{5}{10} = \frac{10}{20}$ $\frac{7}{10} = \frac{14}{20}$

Smallest $\frac{2}{5}$ ⇨ $\frac{5}{10}$ ⇨ $\frac{11}{20}$ ⇨ $\frac{7}{10}$ Largest

The different colours of birds in a flock of flamingos are shown below. Put them in order from most to least common.

$\frac{5}{12}$ are white. $\frac{5}{12} = \frac{10}{24}$ $\frac{6}{24}$ are pink. $\frac{6}{24}$
$\frac{1}{3}$ are green. $\frac{1}{3} = \frac{8}{24}$

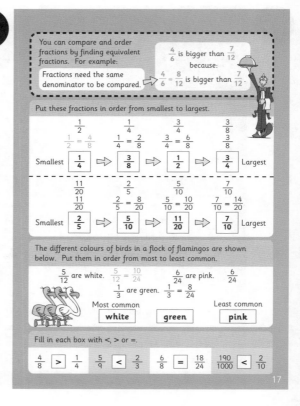

Most common white   green   Least common pink

Fill in each box with <, > or =.

$\frac{4}{8}$ > $\frac{1}{4}$ $\frac{5}{9}$ < $\frac{2}{3}$ $\frac{6}{8}$ = $\frac{18}{24}$ $\frac{190}{1000}$ < $\frac{2}{10}$

17

18 — More Fractions

When fractions have the same denominator, add or subtract just by adding or subtracting the numerators. For example:

$\frac{4}{7} + \frac{2}{7} = \frac{6}{7}$ — The denominators are the same, so just add the numerators.

Write them both with the same denominator first.

$\frac{2}{3} - \frac{1}{6} = ?$

$\frac{2}{3} = \frac{4}{6}$, so $\frac{4}{6} - \frac{1}{6} = \frac{3}{6}$

Answer the following additions and subtractions.

$\frac{7}{9} + \frac{1}{9} = \boxed{\frac{8}{9}}$ $\frac{3}{5} - \frac{2}{5} = \boxed{\frac{1}{5}}$ $\frac{35}{40} - \frac{10}{40} = \boxed{\frac{25}{40}}$

Find equivalent fractions so that you can answer the additions and subtractions.

$\frac{9}{10} - \frac{1}{2} = ?$
$\frac{1}{2} = \frac{5}{10}$, so $\frac{9}{10} - \frac{5}{10} = \boxed{\frac{4}{10}}$

$\frac{1}{4} + \frac{3}{8} = ?$
$\frac{1}{4} = \frac{2}{8}$, so $\frac{2}{8} + \frac{3}{8} = \boxed{\frac{5}{8}}$

$\frac{5}{6} - \frac{1}{3} = ?$
$\frac{1}{3} = \frac{2}{6}$, so $\frac{5}{6} - \frac{2}{6} = \boxed{\frac{3}{6}}$

$\frac{4}{10} + \frac{26}{100} = ?$
$\frac{4}{10} = \frac{40}{100}$, so $\frac{40}{100} + \frac{26}{100} = \boxed{\frac{66}{100}}$

$\frac{5}{12} + \frac{1}{3} = ?$
$\frac{1}{3} = \frac{4}{12}$, so $\frac{5}{12} + \frac{4}{12} = \boxed{\frac{9}{12}}$

$\frac{3}{10} - \frac{7}{1000} = ?$ $\frac{3}{10} = \frac{300}{1000}$,
so $\frac{300}{1000} - \frac{7}{1000} = \boxed{\frac{293}{1000}}$

19

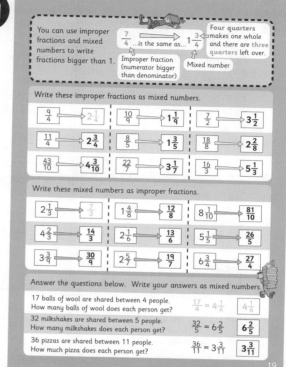

You can use improper fractions and mixed numbers to write fractions bigger than 1.

$\frac{7}{4}$ …is the same as… $1\frac{3}{4}$

Improper fraction (numerator bigger than denominator)   Mixed number

Four quarters makes one whole and there are three quarters left over.

Write these improper fractions as mixed numbers.

$\frac{9}{4} \rightarrow 2\frac{1}{4}$ $\frac{10}{9} \rightarrow 1\frac{1}{9}$ $\frac{7}{2} \rightarrow 3\frac{1}{2}$

$\frac{11}{4} \rightarrow 2\frac{3}{4}$ $\frac{8}{5} \rightarrow 1\frac{3}{5}$ $\frac{18}{8} \rightarrow 2\frac{2}{8}$

$\frac{43}{10} \rightarrow 4\frac{3}{10}$ $\frac{22}{7} \rightarrow 3\frac{1}{7}$ $\frac{16}{3} \rightarrow 5\frac{1}{3}$

Write these mixed numbers as improper fractions.

$2\frac{1}{3} \rightarrow \frac{7}{3}$ $1\frac{4}{8} \rightarrow \frac{12}{8}$ $8\frac{1}{10} \rightarrow \frac{81}{10}$

$4\frac{2}{3} \rightarrow \frac{14}{3}$ $2\frac{1}{6} \rightarrow \frac{13}{6}$ $5\frac{1}{5} \rightarrow \frac{26}{5}$

$3\frac{3}{9} \rightarrow \frac{30}{9}$ $2\frac{5}{7} \rightarrow \frac{19}{7}$ $6\frac{3}{4} \rightarrow \frac{27}{4}$

Answer the questions below. Write your answers as mixed numbers.

17 balls of wool are shared between 4 people. How many balls of wool does each person get?
$\frac{17}{4} = 4\frac{1}{4}$ $\boxed{4\frac{1}{4}}$

32 milkshakes are shared between 5 people. How many milkshakes does each person get?
$\frac{32}{5} = 6\frac{2}{5}$ $\boxed{6\frac{2}{5}}$

36 pizzas are shared between 11 people. How much pizza does each person get?
$\frac{36}{11} = 3\frac{3}{11}$ $\boxed{3\frac{3}{11}}$

20 — Fractions, Decimals and Percentages

"Per cent" means "out of 100". It's written with the per cent sign. So 30% means 30 out of 100, or as a fraction this is.

0.54 is the same as 54%. — To convert from a decimal to a percentage, multiply by 100.

To convert from a fraction to a percentage, find an equivalent fraction over 100, then read off the numerator.

$\frac{2}{5}$ is the same as $\frac{40}{100}$, which is 40%.

To get from a percentage to a decimal, just divide by 100.

39% is the same as 0.39, or $\frac{39}{100}$. — To get from a percentage to a fraction, write it over 100.

Write these decimals as percentages.

0.38 $\boxed{38}$ %   0.72 $\boxed{72}$ %   0.9 $\boxed{90}$ %   0.02 $\boxed{2}$ %

Write these fractions as percentages.

$\frac{6}{10}$ $\boxed{60}$ % $\frac{16}{100}$ $\boxed{16}$ % $\frac{35}{50}$ $\boxed{70}$ % $\frac{7}{25}$ $\boxed{28}$ %

Write these percentages as fractions and decimals.

44% $\boxed{\frac{44}{100}}$ $\boxed{0.44}$ 65% $\boxed{\frac{65}{100}}$ $\boxed{0.65}$ 8% $\boxed{\frac{8}{100}}$ $\boxed{0.08}$

21% $\boxed{\frac{21}{100}}$ $\boxed{0.21}$ 11% $\boxed{\frac{11}{100}}$ $\boxed{0.11}$ 99% $\boxed{\frac{99}{100}}$ $\boxed{0.99}$

21

Learning some common conversions will help you. Here are a few:

$\frac{1}{4} = 25\% = 0.25$ $\frac{1}{2} = 50\% = 0.5$ $\frac{3}{4} = 75\% = 0.75$

$\frac{1}{5} = 20\% = 0.2$ $\frac{3}{5} = 60\% = 0.6$ $\frac{1}{10} = 10\% = 0.1$ $\frac{7}{10} = 70\% = 0.7$

Fill in the missing decimals, fractions and percentages, and shade the shapes to complete the table below.

Percentage	56%	25%	20%	40%
Fraction	$\frac{56}{100}$	$\frac{1}{4}$	$\frac{2}{10}$	$\frac{2}{5}$
Decimal	0.56	0.25	**0.2**	**0.4**
Shaded shape				

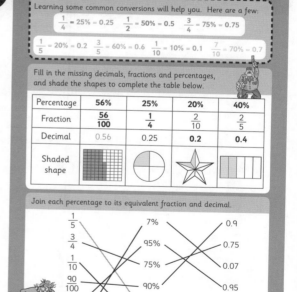

Join each percentage to its equivalent fraction and decimal.

$\frac{1}{5}$ 7%   0.9
$\frac{3}{4}$ 95%   0.75
$\frac{1}{10}$ 75%   0.07
$\frac{90}{100}$ 90%   0.95
$\frac{95}{100}$ 20%   0.1
$\frac{7}{100}$ 10%   0.2

Fractions can be written correctly in different ways. For example, $\frac{1}{4}$ could also be written as $\frac{25}{100}$.

Problem Solving

Some questions don't tell you which calculations to use. You have to choose a good way to work out the answer. Here's an example:

Amir builds one wooden model that is **9.26 cm** tall and another that is **23.7 cm** tall. How much wood does Amir have left over if he had **67.55 cm** to begin with?

Add the first two numbers:
$$\begin{array}{r} 9.26 \\ + 23.7 \\ \hline 3\,2.9\,6 \\ {}_1 \end{array}$$

Then subtract the result from the third number:
$$\begin{array}{r} 6\,\overset{6}{7}.\overset{14}{5}\overset{4}{5} \\ - 32.96 \\ \hline 3\,4.5\,9 \text{ cm} \end{array}$$

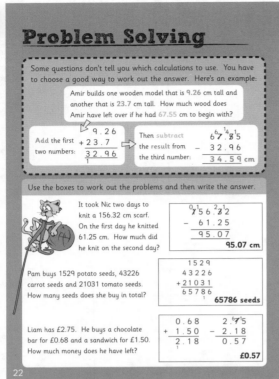

Use the boxes to work out the problems and then write the answer.

It took Nic two days to knit a 156.32 cm scarf. On the first day he knitted 61.25 cm. How much did he knit on the second day?

$$\begin{array}{r} \overset{0}{1}\overset{}{5}\,6.\overset{2}{3}\overset{12}{2} \\ - 61.25 \\ \hline 9\,5.0\,7 \end{array}$$

95.07 cm

Pam buys 1529 potato seeds, 43226 carrot seeds and 21031 tomato seeds. How many seeds does she buy in total?

$$\begin{array}{r} 1529 \\ 43226 \\ + 21031 \\ \hline 65786 \\ {}_1 \end{array}$$

65786 seeds

Liam has £2.75. He buys a chocolate bar for £0.68 and a sandwich for £1.50. How much money does he have left?

$$\begin{array}{r} 0.68 \\ + 1.50 \\ \hline 2.18 \\ {}_1 \end{array} \qquad \begin{array}{r} 2.\overset{6}{7}\overset{1}{5} \\ - 2.18 \\ \hline 0.57 \end{array}$$

£0.57

Use the boxes to work out the problems and then write the answer.

Lily earned £1099 by selling 100 top hats. How much did each top hat cost?

To divide by 100 move the digits two places to the right along the place value columns.

£10.99

A group of 9 friends visit the aquarium. The total cost is £108. How much does each person pay?

$$9\,\overline{|1\,{}^{1}0\,{}^{1}8} \quad \begin{array}{r} 0\,1\,2 \end{array}$$

£12

Each packet of sugar weighs 45 grams. Dan buys 32 packets. How many kilograms of sugar does he have in total?

$$\begin{array}{r} 45 \\ \times\; 32 \\ \hline 90 \\ +1350 \\ \hline 1440 \\ {}_1 \end{array} \qquad 1440 \div 1000 = 1.44$$

1.44 kg

Rob and Sally share a bottle of water. Rob drinks $\frac{1}{4}$ of the bottle, and Sally drinks 20% of the bottle. How much water do they drink in total, as a fraction?

$$\frac{1}{4} = \frac{25}{100}, \; 20\% = \frac{20}{100}$$
$$\frac{25}{100} + \frac{20}{100} = \frac{45}{100}$$

Egg boxes can hold 6 eggs. Helen has 226 eggs. She fills boxes with eggs until she can't fill any more. How many eggs aren't in boxes?

$$6\,\overline{|2\,{}^{2}2\,{}^{4}6} \quad \begin{array}{r} 0\,3\,7\,r\,4 \end{array}$$

4 eggs

Ant and Dave each buy the same size pizza. Ant cuts his into 12 slices and eats 4 slices. Dave cuts his into 6 slices and eats an equivalent amount to Ant. Write how many slices Dave has eaten.

$$\frac{4}{12} \;\overset{\div 2}{\underset{\div 2}{=}}\; \frac{2}{6}$$

2 slices

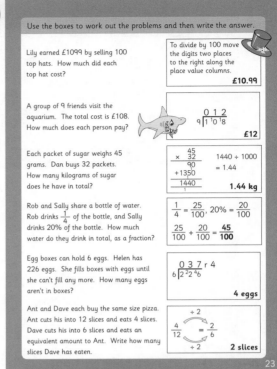

If your child has made a few mistakes, remind them to double check their work next time — it's a really good habit for them to get into.

Rounding & Estimating

Round **up** if a number is **5 or bigger**, and round **down** if it's **less than 5**. Here's an example:

45.39 rounded to 1 decimal place is **45.4** because the 9 is bigger than 5. Rounded to the nearest whole number it's **45**, because the 3 is less than 5.

You can round numbers to the nearest 10, 100 or 1000 to get an estimate. This will give you a rough idea of the right answer:

Estimate 5781.4 + 1938.

Round to the nearest 1000.

5781.4 ≈ 6000, 1938 ≈ 2000.
6000 + 2000 = **8000**.

≈ means 'approximately equal to'.

Round each number to 1 decimal place and to the nearest whole number.

	1 d.p.	whole		1 d.p.	whole		1 d.p.	whole
3.82	3.8	4	25.19	25.2	25	99.57	99.6	100
168.28	168.3	168	87.47	87.5	87	355.85	355.9	356

Use estimating to decide if these calculations look correct. Put a tick or a cross in the box next to the calculation.

8198 − 2287 = 5911 ✓
8000 − 2000 = 6000

152 + 689 + 302 = 1911 ✗
200 + 700 + 300 = 1200

97.2 × 41.8 = 406.296 ✗
100 × 40 = 4000

47.5 × 39.7 = 1885.75 ✓
50 × 40 = 2000

3082.6 + 7154.62 = 10237.22 ✓
3000 + 7000 = 10000

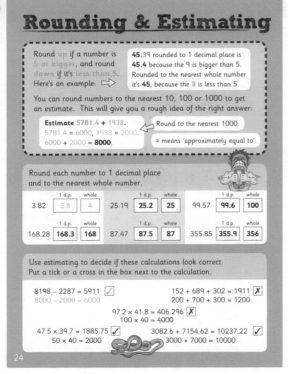

Units & Measures

Metric units come in multiples of **10, 100** and **1000**. For example:

1 cm = 10 mm	1 kg = 1000 g
1 m = 100 cm	1 l = 1000 ml
1 km = 1000 m	

How many metres in 5.3 km?
1 km = 1000 m, so 5.3 km = 5.3 × 1000 = 5300 m

You can use approximations to convert between metric and imperial.

5 cm ≈ 2 inches	1 kg ≈ 2 pounds
1 m ≈ 3 feet	25 g ≈ 1 ounce
8 km ≈ 5 miles	1 l ≈ 2 pints

What is 6 pounds in kilograms?
6 pounds is 3 lots of 2 pounds. 3 lots of 1 kg is **3 kg**.

Answer the questions below.

A bucket holds 3000 ml. What's this in litres?	3000 ÷ 1000 = 3 l	3 l
How many cm are in 2 m?	2 × 100 = 200 cm.	**200 cm**
A tin of soup weighs 600 g. What's this in kilograms?	600 ÷ 1000 = 0.6 kg	**0.6 kg**

Use the approximations above to answer the questions.

How many feet are in 8 m?	8 × 3 = 24 feet	**24 feet**
A barrel holds 160 l. What's this in pints?	160 × 2 = 320 pints	**320 pints**
A running race is 25 miles. What's this in km?	25 miles is 5 lots of 5 miles. 5 lots of 8 km is 40 km.	**40 km**
A designer uses 35 cm of ribbon. How many inches is this?	35 cm is 7 lots of 5 cm. 7 lots of 2 inches is 14 inches.	**14 inches**

For extra practice on measurements, you could show your child items from your food cupboard and get them to convert their mass or volume into different units.

Perimeter, Area & Volume

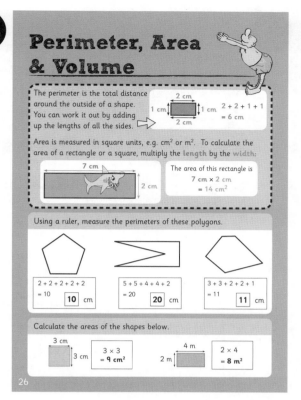

The perimeter is the total distance around the outside of a shape. You can work it out by adding up the lengths of all the sides.

2 + 2 + 1 + 1 = 6 cm

Area is measured in square units, e.g. cm² or m². To calculate the area of a rectangle or a square, multiply the **length** by the **width**:

The area of this rectangle is
7 cm × 2 cm
= 14 cm²

Using a ruler, measure the perimeters of these polygons.

2 + 2 + 2 + 2 + 2
= 10   **10** cm

5 + 5 + 4 + 4 + 2
= 20   **20** cm

3 + 3 + 2 + 2 + 1
= 11   **11** cm

Calculate the areas of the shapes below.

3 cm
3 cm   3 × 3 = **9 cm²**

4 m
2 m   2 × 4 = **8 m²**

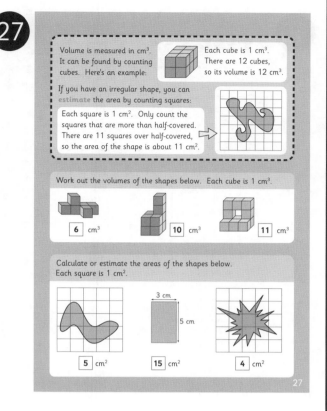

Volume is measured in cm³. It can be found by counting cubes. Here's an example:

Each cube is 1 cm³. There are 12 cubes, so its volume is 12 cm³.

If you have an irregular shape, you can **estimate** the area by counting squares:

Each square is 1 cm². Only count the squares that are more than half-covered. There are 11 squares over half-covered, so the area of the shape is about 11 cm².

Work out the volumes of the shapes below. Each cube is 1 cm³.

6 cm³   **10** cm³   **11** cm³

Calculate or estimate the areas of the shapes below. Each square is 1 cm².

5 cm²   3 cm / 5 cm **15** cm²   **4** cm²

Angles

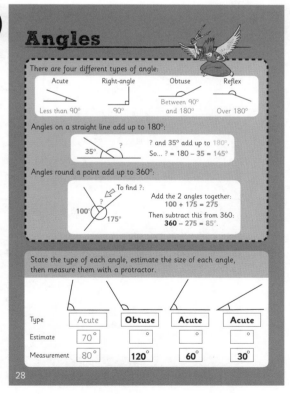

There are four different types of angle:

Acute — Less than 90°
Right-angle — 90°
Obtuse — Between 90° and 180°
Reflex — Over 180°

Angles on a straight line add up to 180°:

35°   ? and 35° add up to 180°.
So... ? = 180 − 35 = 145°

Angles round a point add up to 360°:

To find ?:
Add the 2 angles together:
100 + 175 = 275
100° 175°
Then subtract this from 360:
360 − 275 = 85°.

State the type of each angle, estimate the size of each angle, then measure them with a protractor.

Type	Acute	**Obtuse**	**Acute**	**Acute**
Estimate	70°	°	°	°
Measurement	80°	**120°**	**60°**	**30°**

Calculate the missing angles without using a protractor.

65° A   90° 75° B   65° C 70°

180 − 65 = 115
A = 115°

90 + 75 = 165
180 − 165 = 15
B = **15°**

70 + 65 = 135
180 − 135 = 45
C = **45°**

Work out the missing angle between the hands on the clocks. Write your answer in the boxes.

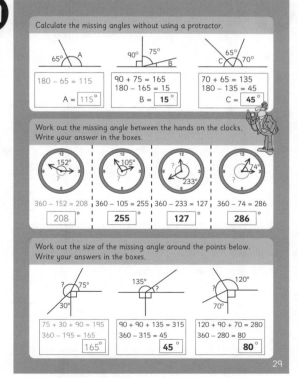

152°   105°   233°   74°

360 − 152 = 208
208°

360 − 105 = 255
255°

360 − 233 = 127
127°

360 − 74 = 286
286°

Work out the size of the missing angle around the points below. Write your answers in the boxes.

75° 30°   135°   120° 70°

75 + 30 + 90 = 195
360 − 195 = 165
165°

90 + 90 + 135 = 315
360 − 315 = 45
45°

120 + 90 + 70 = 280
360 − 280 = 80
80°

If needed, your child can use the column methods for adding and subtracting angles.

Tables and Charts

Tables, graphs and charts can be used to show information. Here's an example:

What was the temperature at 16:00?
Find 16:00 on the horizontal axis. Read up to the line.
Then read across to find the temperature = **7 °C**.

Waleed and Gail measure their height every year. Plot their results in the table as a line graph. Use a different colour for each line.

Age	Waleed's height (cm)	Gail's height (cm)
8	115	117.5
9	120	125
10	125	132.5
11	132.5	137.5
12	140	145
13	145	152.5

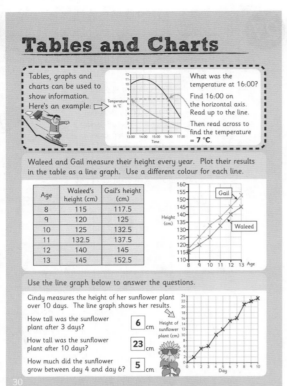

Use the line graph below to answer the questions.

Cindy measures the height of her sunflower plant over 10 days. The line graph shows her results.

How tall was the sunflower plant after 3 days? **6** cm

How tall was the sunflower plant after 10 days? **23** cm

How much did the sunflower grow between day 4 and day 6? **5** cm

Timetables are really useful for things such as buses and trains. They often show times with the 24-hour clock. For example:

When does the 12:50 bus from Heath Hayes arrive at Burntwood?

Cannock	10:55	12:41	13:06	15:28
Heath Hayes	11:04	12:50	13:15	15:37
Norton Canes	11:09	12:55	13:20	15:42
Burntwood	11:18	13:04	13:29	15:51
Lichfield	11:36	13:22	13:47	16:09

Find the **12:50 bus** from Heath Hayes, and read down to the **Burntwood** row. It's at **13:04**.

The timetable shows train times. Use it to answer the questions.

Birmingham	15:42	16:30	17:02	19:51
Solihull	15:50	16:38	17:10	19:59
Warwick	16:01	16:49	17:21	20:10
Leamington	16:07	16:55	17:27	20:16
Canley	16:11	16:59	17:31	20:20

When is the last train from Warwick? **20:10**

How long does it take to get from Birmingham to Canley? **29 mins**

Jimmy needs to be in Leamington before 5 o'clock. What time should he get the train from Solihull? **16:38**

The table shows the times that four cyclists finished each lap of a race. Use the table to answer the questions.

What time did Billy finish Lap 2? **10:36**

Who was the third person to finish Lap 2? **Ruth**

	Ruth	Billy	Tara	Niko
Lap 1	09:03	08:36	09:11	09:35
Lap 2	10:59	10:36	10:44	11:21
Lap 3	12:44	12:41	13:02	14:07
Lap 4	15:15	15:20	16:01	17:24

How many riders had completed Lap 4 before 4 pm? **2**

Which rider took over 3 hours to complete Lap 4? **Niko**

Reflections

You can reflect a shape or pattern in a horizontal or a vertical mirror line. Here's an example:

Shape A reflects in the **horizontal** mirror line to become Shape B. Shape A reflects in the **vertical** mirror line to become Shape C.

Each point and its reflection are the same distance from the mirror line.

Reflect Shape X in the horizontal mirror line and label it Shape Y. Then reflect Shape Y in the vertical mirror line and label it Shape Z.

Join shapes that have been reflected horizontally with a solid line, and join shapes that have been reflected vertically with a dashed line.

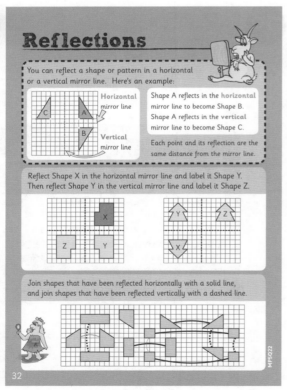

MP5022

If your child has difficulty with reflections, try tracing the shape onto some tracing paper, then fold the paper along the mirror line.

Rockets & Comets

You'll need a counter for each player and a dice. Place your counters on the first square, and take it in turns to roll the dice once. Follow the instructions when you land on them.

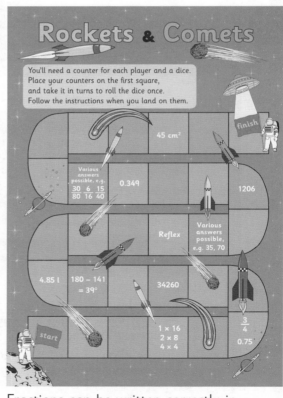

Fractions can be written correctly in different ways. For example, $\frac{3}{4}$ could also be written as $\frac{75}{100}$.

You can compare and order fractions by finding equivalent fractions. For example:

Fractions need the same denominator to be compared.

$\frac{4}{6}$ is bigger than $\frac{7}{12}$ because:

$\frac{4}{6} = \frac{8}{12}$ is bigger than $\frac{7}{12}$.

Put these fractions in order from smallest to largest.

$\frac{1}{2}$ $\frac{1}{4}$ $\frac{3}{4}$ $\frac{3}{8}$

$\frac{1}{2} = \frac{4}{8}$

Smallest ☐ ⇨ ☐ ⇨ ☐ ⇨ ☐ Largest

$\frac{11}{20}$ $\frac{2}{5}$ $\frac{5}{10}$ $\frac{7}{10}$

Smallest ☐ ⇨ ☐ ⇨ ☐ ⇨ ☐ Largest

The different colours of birds in a flock of flamingos are shown below. Put them in order from most to least common.

$\frac{5}{12}$ are white. $\frac{5}{12} = \frac{10}{24}$ $\frac{6}{24}$ are pink.

$\frac{1}{3}$ are green.

Most common ☐   ☐   Least common ☐

Fill in each box with <, > or =.

$\frac{4}{8}$ ☐ $\frac{1}{4}$ $\frac{5}{9}$ ☐ $\frac{2}{3}$ $\frac{6}{8}$ ☐ $\frac{18}{24}$ $\frac{190}{1000}$ ☐ $\frac{2}{10}$

17

More Fractions

When fractions have the same denominator, add or subtract just by adding or subtracting the numerators. For example:

$$\frac{4}{7} + \frac{2}{7} = \frac{6}{7}$$

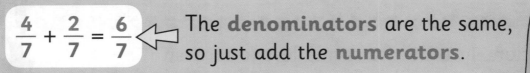

The **denominators** are the same, so just add the **numerators**.

Write them both with the same **denominator** first.

$$\frac{2}{3} - \frac{1}{6} = ?$$

$$\frac{2}{3} = \frac{4}{6}, \text{ so } \frac{4}{6} - \frac{1}{6} = \frac{3}{6}$$

Answer the following additions and subtractions.

$$\frac{7}{9} + \frac{1}{9} = \boxed{\frac{8}{9}}$$

$$\frac{3}{5} - \frac{2}{5} = \boxed{}$$

$$\frac{35}{40} - \frac{10}{40} = \boxed{}$$

Find equivalent fractions so that you can answer the additions and subtractions.

$$\frac{9}{10} - \frac{1}{2} = ?$$

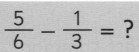

$$\frac{1}{2} = \frac{5}{10}, \text{ so } \frac{9}{10} - \frac{5}{10} = \boxed{\frac{4}{10}}$$

$$\frac{1}{4} + \frac{3}{8} = ?$$
$$\boxed{}$$

$$\frac{5}{6} - \frac{1}{3} = ?$$
$$\boxed{}$$

$$\frac{4}{10} + \frac{26}{100} = ?$$
$$\boxed{}$$

$$\frac{5}{12} + \frac{1}{3} = ?$$

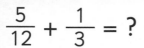

$$\boxed{}$$

$$\frac{3}{10} - \frac{7}{1000} = ?$$
$$\boxed{}$$

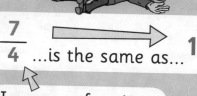

You can use improper fractions and mixed numbers to write fractions bigger than 1.

$\frac{7}{4}$ ...is the same as... $1\frac{3}{4}$

Four quarters makes one whole and there are **three quarters** left over.

Improper fraction (numerator bigger than denominator)

Mixed number

Write these improper fractions as mixed numbers.

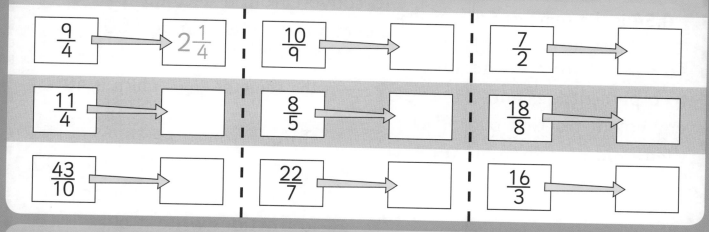

$\frac{9}{4}$ → $2\frac{1}{4}$

$\frac{10}{9}$ →

$\frac{7}{2}$ →

$\frac{11}{4}$ →

$\frac{8}{5}$ →

$\frac{18}{8}$ →

$\frac{43}{10}$ →

$\frac{22}{7}$ →

$\frac{16}{3}$ →

Write these mixed numbers as improper fractions.

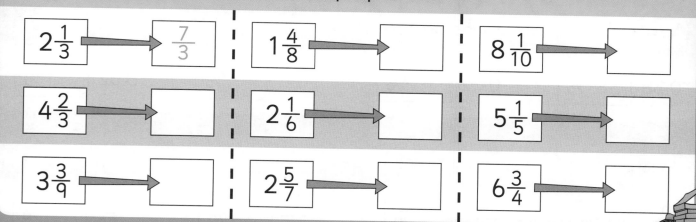

$2\frac{1}{3}$ → $\frac{7}{3}$

$1\frac{4}{8}$ →

$8\frac{1}{10}$ →

$4\frac{2}{3}$ →

$2\frac{1}{6}$ →

$5\frac{1}{5}$ →

$3\frac{3}{9}$ →

$2\frac{5}{7}$ →

$6\frac{3}{4}$ →

Answer the questions below. Write your answers as mixed numbers.

17 balls of wool are shared between 4 people. How many balls of wool does each person get?

$\frac{17}{4} = 4\frac{1}{4}$ $4\frac{1}{4}$

32 milkshakes are shared between 5 people. How many milkshakes does each person get?

36 pizzas are shared between 11 people. How much pizza does each person get?

19

Fractions, Decimals and Percentages

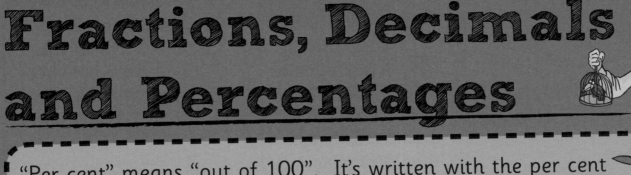

"Per cent" means "out of 100". It's written with the per cent sign %. So 30% means 30 out of 100, or as a fraction this is $\frac{30}{100}$.

0.54 is the same as **54%**. ⟵ To convert from a decimal to a percentage, multiply by 100.

To convert from a fraction to a percentage, find an equivalent fraction over 100, then read off the numerator. ⟹ $\frac{2}{5}$ is the same as $\frac{40}{100}$, which is **40%**.

To get from a percentage to a decimal, just divide by 100.

39% is the same as **0.39**, or $\frac{39}{100}$. ⟵ To get from a percentage to a fraction, write it over 100.

Write these decimals as percentages.

0.38 | **38 %**   0.72 | %   0.9 | %   0.02 | %

Write these fractions as percentages.

$\frac{6}{10}$ | **60 %** $\frac{16}{100}$ | % $\frac{35}{50}$ | % $\frac{7}{25}$ | %

Write these percentages as fractions and decimals.

44% | $\frac{44}{100}$ | 0.44   65% | ☐ | ☐   8% | ☐ | ☐

21% | ☐ | ☐   11% | ☐ | ☐   99% | ☐ | ☐

Learning some common conversions will help you. Here are a few:

$$\frac{1}{4} = 25\% = 0.25 \qquad \frac{1}{2} = 50\% = 0.5 \qquad \frac{3}{4} = 75\% = 0.75$$

$$\frac{1}{5} = 20\% = 0.2 \qquad \frac{3}{5} = 60\% = 0.6 \qquad \frac{1}{10} = 10\% = 0.1 \qquad \frac{7}{10} = 70\% = 0.7$$

Fill in the missing decimals, fractions and percentages, and shade the shapes to complete the table below.

Percentage				
Fraction			$\frac{2}{10}$	$\frac{2}{5}$
Decimal	0.56	0.25		
Shaded shape				

Join each percentage to its equivalent fraction and decimal.

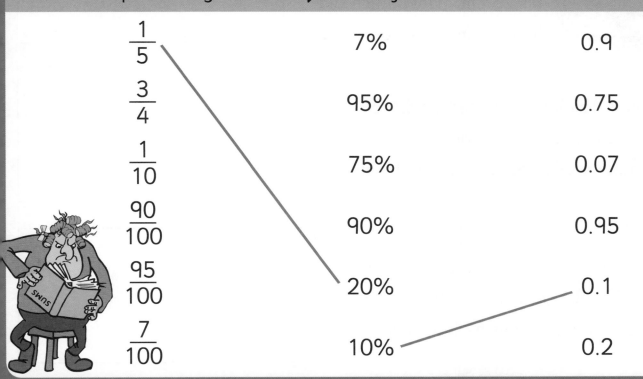

$\frac{1}{5}$ 7%   0.9

$\frac{3}{4}$ 95%   0.75

$\frac{1}{10}$ 75%   0.07

$\frac{90}{100}$ 90%   0.95

$\frac{95}{100}$ 20%   0.1

$\frac{7}{100}$ 10%   0.2

21

Problem Solving

Some questions don't tell you which calculations to use. You have to choose a good way to work out the answer. Here's an example:

> Amir builds one wooden model that is **9.26** cm tall and another that is **23.7** cm tall. How much wood does Amir have left over if he had **67.55** cm to begin with?

Add the first two numbers:

```
   9 . 2 6
+ 2 3 . 7
---------
 3 2 . 9 6
   1
```

Then **subtract** the **result** from the third number:

```
  6⁶7̶.¹4̶3̶¹5
-  3 2 . 9 6
-----------
  3 4 . 5 9  cm
```

Use the boxes to work out the problems and then write the answer.

It took Nic two days to knit a 156.32 cm scarf. On the first day he knitted 61.25 cm. How much did he knit on the second day?

Pam buys 1529 potato seeds, 43226 carrot seeds and 21031 tomato seeds. How many seeds does she buy in total?

Liam has £2.75. He buys a chocolate bar for £0.68 and a sandwich for £1.50. How much money does he have left?

Lily earned £1099 by selling 100 top hats. How much did each top hat cost?

A group of 9 friends visit the aquarium. The total cost is £108. How much does each person pay?

Each packet of sugar weighs 45 grams. Dan buys 32 packets. How many kilograms of sugar does he have in total?

Rob and Sally share a bottle of water. Rob drinks $\frac{1}{4}$ of the bottle, and Sally drinks 20% of the bottle. How much water do they drink in total, as a fraction?

Egg boxes can hold 6 eggs. Helen has 226 eggs. She fills boxes with eggs until she can't fill any more. How many eggs aren't in boxes?

Ant and Dave each buy the same size pizza. Ant cuts his into 12 slices and eats 4 slices. Dave cuts his into 6 slices and eats an equivalent amount to Ant. Write how many slices Dave has eaten.

Rounding & Estimating

Round **up** if a number is **5 or bigger**, and round **down** if it's **less than 5**. Here's an example: ⇨

45.39 rounded to 1 decimal place is **45.4** because the **9** is bigger than 5. Rounded to the nearest whole number it's **45**, because the **3** is less than 5.

You can round numbers to the nearest 10, 100 or 1000 to get an estimate. This will give you a rough idea of the right answer:

Estimate 5781.4 + 1938.
5781.4 ≈ 6000, 1938 ≈ 2000.
6000 + 2000 = **8000**.

Round to the nearest 1000.

≈ means 'approximately equal to'.

Round each number to 1 decimal place and to the nearest whole number.

	1 d.p.	whole
3.82	3.8	4

	1 d.p.	whole
25.19		

	1 d.p.	whole
99.57		

	1 d.p.	whole
168.28		

	1 d.p.	whole
87.47		

	1 d.p.	whole
355.85		

Use estimating to decide if these calculations look correct.
Put a tick or a cross in the box next to the calculation.

8198 − 2287 = 5911 ✓
8000 − 2000 = 6000

152 + 689 + 302 = 1911 ☐

97.2 × 41.8 = 406.296 ☐

47.5 × 39.7 = 1885.75 ☐

3082.6 + 7154.62 = 10237.22 ☐

Units & Measures

Metric units come in multiples of **10**, **100** and **1000**. For example:

1 cm = **10 mm**

1 m = **100 cm**

1 km = **1000 m**

1 kg = **1000 g**

1 l = **1000 ml**

How many metres in 5.3 km?

1 km = 1000 m, so 5.3 km = 5.3 × 1000 = **5300 m**

You can use approximations to convert between metric and imperial.

5 cm ≈ 2 **inches**

1 m ≈ 3 **feet**

8 km ≈ 5 **miles**

1 kg ≈ 2 **pounds**

25 g ≈ 1 **ounce**

1 l ≈ 2 **pints**

What is 6 pounds in kilograms? 6 pounds is 3 lots of 2 pounds. 3 lots of 1 kg is **3 kg**.

Answer the questions below.

A bucket holds 3000 ml. What's this in litres?	3000 ÷ 1000 = 3 l	3 l
How many cm are in 2 m?		
A tin of soup weighs 600 g. What's this in kilograms?		

Use the approximations above to answer the questions.

How many feet are in 8 m?	
A barrel holds 160 l. What's this in pints?	
A running race is 25 miles. What's this in km?	
A designer uses 35 cm of ribbon. How many inches is this?	

Perimeter, Area & Volume

The perimeter is the total distance around the outside of a shape. You can work it out by adding up the lengths of all the sides.

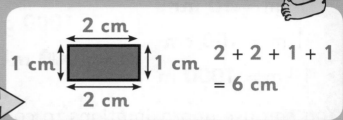

2 cm

1 cm   1 cm

2 cm

2 + 2 + 1 + 1 = 6 cm

Area is measured in square units, e.g. cm² or m². To calculate the area of a rectangle or a square, multiply the **length** by the **width**:

7 cm

2 cm

The area of this rectangle is

7 cm × 2 cm

= 14 cm²

Using a ruler, measure the perimeters of these polygons.

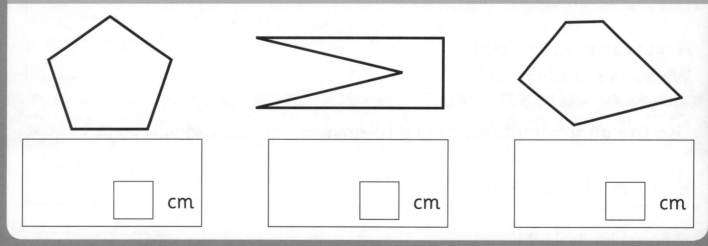

| | cm | | cm | | cm |

Calculate the areas of the shapes below.

3 cm

3 cm

4 m

2 m

Volume is measured in cm³. It can be found by counting cubes. Here's an example:

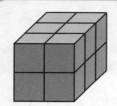

Each cube is 1 cm³. There are 12 cubes, so its volume is 12 cm³.

If you have an irregular shape, you can **estimate** the area by counting squares:

Each square is 1 cm². Only count the squares that are more than half-covered. There are 11 squares over half-covered, so the area of the shape is about 11 cm².

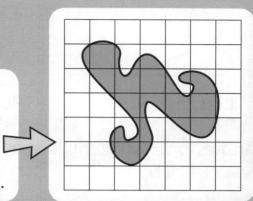

Work out the volumes of the shapes below. Each cube is 1 cm³.

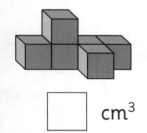

☐ cm³

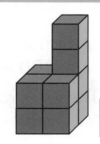

☐ cm³

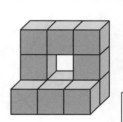

☐ cm³

Calculate or estimate the areas of the shapes below. Each square is 1 cm².

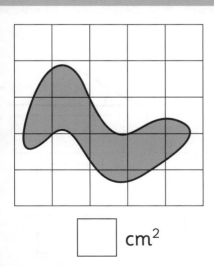

☐ cm²

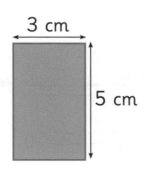
3 cm
5 cm

☐ cm²

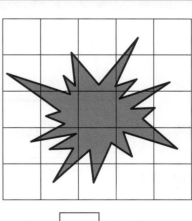

☐ cm²

27

Angles

There are four different types of angle:

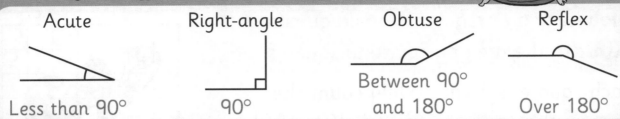

Acute	Right-angle	Obtuse	Reflex
Less than 90°	90°	Between 90° and 180°	Over 180°

Angles on a straight line add up to 180°:

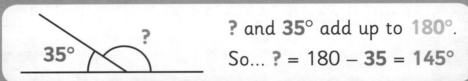

35°   **?**

? and **35°** add up to **180°**.

So... **?** = 180 − **35** = **145°**

Angles round a point add up to 360°:

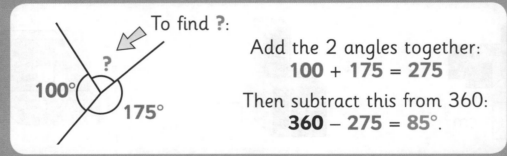

To find **?**:

100°   **?**   **175°**

Add the 2 angles together:
100 + 175 = 275

Then subtract this from 360:
360 − 275 = 85°.

State the type of each angle, estimate the size of each angle, then measure them with a protractor.

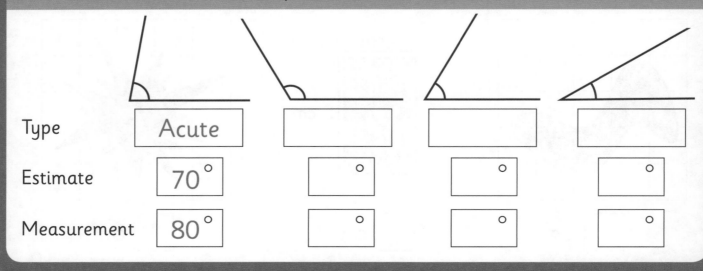

Type	Acute			
Estimate	70°	°	°	°
Measurement	80°	°	°	°

Calculate the missing angles without using a protractor.

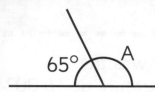

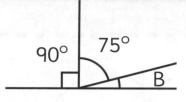

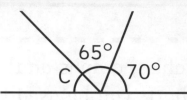

180 − 65 = 115		
A = 115°	B = ___ °	C = ___ °

Work out the missing angle between the hands on the clocks. Write your answer in the boxes.

360 − 152 = 208

208 °

___ °   ___ °   ___ °

Work out the size of the missing angle around the points below. Write your answers in the boxes.

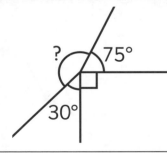

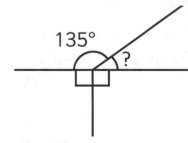

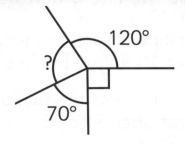

75 + 30 + 90 = 195
360 − 195 = 165
165°

___ °   ___ °

Tables and Charts

Tables, graphs and charts can be used to show information.
Here's an example: ⟹

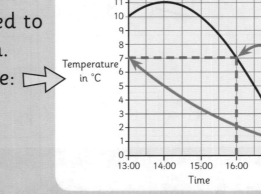

What was the temperature at 16:00?

Find 16:00 on the horizontal axis. Read up to the line.

Then read across to find the temperature = **7 °C**.

Waleed and Gail measure their height every year. Plot their results in the table as a line graph. Use a different colour for each line.

Age	Waleed's height (cm)	Gail's height (cm)
8	115	117.5
9	120	125
10	125	132.5
11	132.5	137.5
12	140	145
13	145	152.5

Use the line graph below to answer the questions.

Cindy measures the height of her sunflower plant over 10 days. The line graph shows her results.

How tall was the sunflower plant after 3 days? ☐ cm

How tall was the sunflower plant after 10 days? ☐ cm

How much did the sunflower grow between day 4 and day 6? ☐ cm

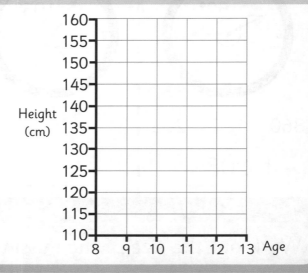

Timetables are really useful for things such as buses and trains.
They often show times with the 24-hour clock. For example:

When does the
12:50 bus from
Heath Hayes arrive
at Burntwood?

Cannock	10:55	12:41	13:06	15:28
Heath Hayes	11:04	12:50	13:15	15:37
Norton Canes	11:09	12:55	13:20	15:42
Burntwood	11:18	13:04	13:29	15:51
Lichfield	11:36	13:22	13:47	16:09

Find the **12:50 bus** from Heath Hayes,
and read down to the **Burntwood** row. ⟶   It's at **13:04**.

The timetable shows train times. Use it to answer the questions.

Birmingham	15:42	16:30	17:02	19:51
Solihull	15:50	16:38	17:10	19:59
Warwick	16:01	16:49	17:21	20:10
Leamington	16:07	16:55	17:27	20:16
Canley	16:11	16:59	17:31	20:20

When is the last
train from Warwick?

How long does it take to get from Birmingham to Canley?

Jimmy needs to be in Leamington before 5 o'clock.
What time should he get the train from Solihull?

The table shows the times that four cyclists finished each
lap of a race. Use the table to answer the questions.

What time did Billy
finish Lap 2?

	Ruth	Billy	Tara	Niko
Lap 1	09:03	08:36	09:11	09:35
Lap 2	10:59	10:36	10:44	11:21
Lap 3	12:44	12:41	13:02	14:07
Lap 4	15:15	15:20	16:01	17:24

Who was the third
person to finish Lap 2?

How many riders had completed Lap 4 before 4 pm?

Which rider took over 3 hours to complete Lap 4?

Reflections

You can reflect a shape or pattern in a horizontal or a vertical mirror line. Here's an example:

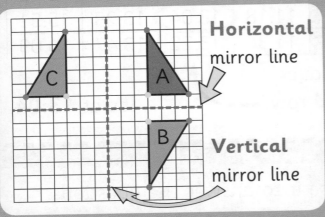

Horizontal mirror line

Vertical mirror line

Shape A reflects in the **horizontal** mirror line to become Shape B. Shape A reflects in the **vertical** mirror line to become Shape C.

Each point and its reflection are the same distance from the mirror line.

Reflect Shape X in the horizontal mirror line and label it Shape Y. Then reflect Shape Y in the vertical mirror line and label it Shape Z.

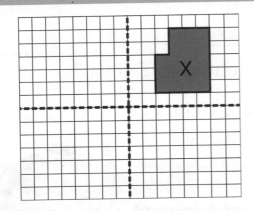

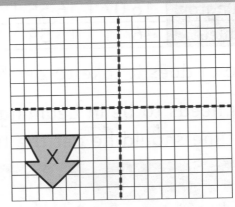

Join shapes that have been reflected horizontally with a solid line, and join shapes that have been reflected vertically with a dashed line.

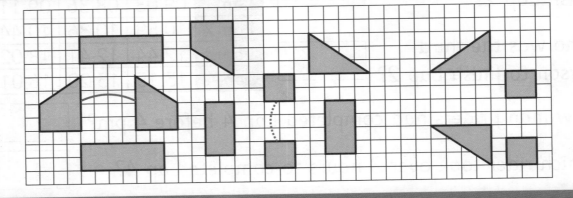